Sing a Sweet Song

AUTHORS

Elaine Mei Aoki
Virginia A. Arnold
James Flood
James V. Hoffman
Diane Lapp
Miriam Martinez
Annemarie Sullivan Palincsar
Michael Priestley
Nancy Roser
Carl B. Smith
William H. Teale
Josefina Villamil Tinajero
Arnold W. Webb
Peggy E. Williams
Karen D. Wood

MACMILLAN/McGRAW-HILL SCHOOL PUBLISHING COMPANY

NEW YORK CHICAGO COLUMBUS

AUTHORS, CONSULTANTS, AND REVIEWERS

WRITE IDEA! Authors

Elaine Mei Aoki, James Flood, James V. Hoffman, Diane Lapp, Ana Huerta Macias, Miriam Martinez, Ann McCallum, Michael Priestley, Nancy Roser, Carl B. Smith, William Strong, William H. Teale, Charles Temple, Josefina Villamil Tinajero, Arnold W. Webb, Peggy E. Williams

The approach to writing in Macmillan/McGraw-Hill Reading/Language Arts is based on the strategies and approaches to composition and conventions of language in Macmillan/McGraw-Hill's writing-centered language arts program, WRITE IDEA!

Multicultural and Educational Consultants

Alma Flor Ada, Yvonne Beamer, Joyce Buckner, Helen Gillotte, Cheryl Hudson, Narcita Medina, Lorraine Monroe, James R. Murphy, Sylvia Peña, Joseph B. Rubin, Ramon Santiago, Cliff Trafzer, Hai Tran, Esther Lee Yao

Literature Consultants

Ashley Bryan, Joan I. Glazer, Paul Janeczko, Margaret H. Lippert

International Consultants

Edward B. Adams, Barbara Johnson, Raymond L. Marshall

Music and Audio Consultants

John Farrell, Marilyn C. Davidson, Vincent Lawrence, Sarah Pirtle, Susan R. Snyder, Rick and Deborah Witkowski

Teacher Reviewers

Terry Baker, Jane Bauer, James Bedi, Nora Bickel, Vernell Bowen, Donald Cason, Jean Chaney, Carolyn Clark, Alan Cox, Kathryn DesCarpentrie, Carol L. Ellis, Roberta Gale, Brenda Huffman, Erma Inscore, Sharon Kidwell, Elizabeth Love, Isabel Marcus, Elaine McCraney, Michelle Moraros, Earlene Parr, Dr. Richard Potts, Jeanette Pulliam, Michael Rubin, Henrietta Sakamaki, Kathleen Cultron Sanders, Belinda Snow, Dr. Jayne Steubing, Margaret Mary Sulentic, Barbara Tate, Seretta Vincent, Willard Waite, Barbara Wilson, Veronica York

ACKNOWLEDGMENTS

The publisher gratefully acknowledges permission to reprint the following copyrighted material:

"The Bed" from THE TIGER AND THE RABBIT by Pura Belpré. Copyright © 1944 Pura Belpré. Used by permission of Eliseo Torres.

"The Butterfly" by Clinton Scollard is from *Child Life Magazine*. Copyright 1924, 1952 by Rand McNally & Company. Reprinted by permission of the publisher.

"By Myself" is the text and art from HONEY, I LOVE by Eloise Greenfield. Illustrated by Diane and Leo Dillon. Text copyright © 1978 by Eloise Greenfield. Illustrations copyright © 1978 by Diane and Leo Dillon. Reprinted by permission of HarperCollins Publishers.

"The Great Big Enormous Turnip" with pictures by Helen Oxenbury and story by Alexei Tolstoy. Copyright © 1968 Helen Oxenbury. Reprinted by permission of Octopus Children's Publishing.

"The Gunnywolf" is the entire text and art from THE GUNNYWOLF by A. Delaney. Copyright © 1988 by A. Delaney. Reprinted by permission of HarperCollins Publishers.

"In the Attic" by Hiawyn Oram and illustrated by Satoshi Kitamura. Text copyright © 1984 by Hiawyn Oram. Illustrations copyright © 1984 by Satoshi Kitamura. Permission to reprint and record granted by Henry Holt and Company Inc.

"Jimmy Lee Did It" written and illustrated by Pat Cummings. Copyright © 1985 by Pat Cummings. Reprinted by permission of Lothrop, Lee & Shepard, a division of William Morrow and Company, Inc. Publishers, New York.

"The Line Sophie Drew" by Peter and Susan Barrett with illustrations by Peter Barrett. Copyright © 1972 by Peter and Susan Barrett. Reprinted by permission of Scroll Press, Inc.

"The Missing Tarts" from THE MISSING TARTS by B. G. Hennessy. Text copyright © 1989 by B. G. Hennessy. Illustrations copyright © 1989 by Tracey Campbell Pearson. Used by permission of Viking Penguin, a division of Penguin Books USA Inc.

"Pretending" from UPSIDE DOWN AND INSIDE OUT: POEMS FOR ALL YOUR POCKETS by Bobbi Katz. Copyright © 1973 by Bobbi Katz. Used by permission of the author who controls all rights.

"The Trek" written and illustrated by Ann Jonas. Copyright © 1985 by Ann Jonas. Reprinted by permission of Greenwillow Books, a division of William Morrow and Company, Inc., Publishers, New York.

"Worlds I Know" is excerpted from "Worlds I Know" in WORLDS I KNOW AND OTHER POEMS by Myra Cohn Livingston. Copyright © 1985 by Myra Cohn Livingston. Reprinted by permission of Margaret K. McElderry Books, an imprint of Macmillan Publishing Company.

COVER DESIGN: WYD Design
COVER ILLUSTRATION: Lynn Rowe Reed

DESIGN CREDITS
Sheldon Cotler + Associates Editorial Group, *Glossary*
WYD Design, 8-11, 126-129
Designframe Incorporated, 78-79, 194-195
Notovitz Design Inc., *Information Illustrated*

ILLUSTRATION CREDITS
Unit 1: Sue Ellen Brown, 8-11; Susan Swan, 40-43; Marilyn Janovitz, 76-77;
(Continued on page 264)

Macmillan/McGraw-Hill School Division
10 Union Square East
New York, New York 10003

Printed in the United States of America
ISBN 0-02-178754-9 / 1, L.4
3 4 5 6 7 8 9 RRW 99 98 97 96 95 94 93

Dedication from the Development Team. . .

To our staff, whose names do not appear in this book, but whose skill, dedication to excellence, and commitment to the children we serve, resonate from cover to cover.

Beverly Silver *Karen Kearns-O'Sullivan*

UNIT 1

TELL ME A STORY

Poetry

More to Explore

Books from the Classroom Library

JUST IMAGINE!

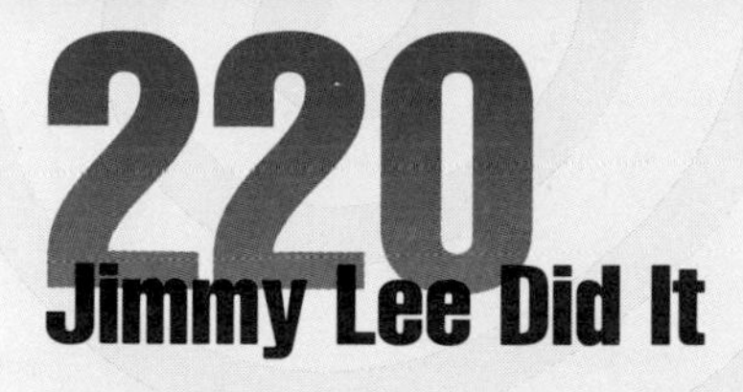

Poetry

More to Explore

Books from the Classroom Library

CONTENTS

UNIT
1
TELL ME
A STORY
The Princes

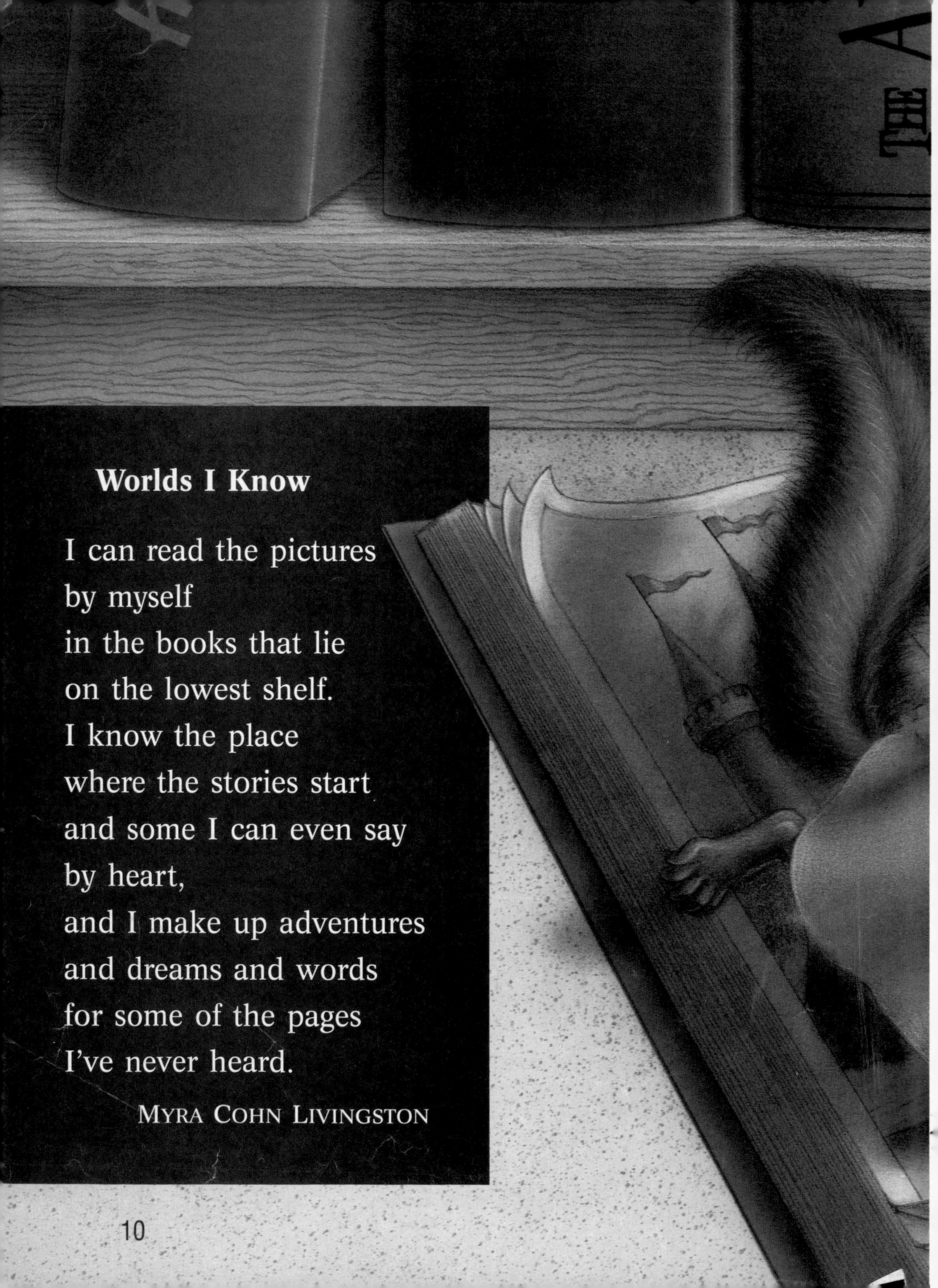

Worlds I Know

I can read the pictures
by myself
in the books that lie
on the lowest shelf.
I know the place
where the stories start
and some I can even say
by heart,
and I make up adventures
and dreams and words
for some of the pages
I've never heard.

MYRA COHN LIVINGSTON

THE GREAT BIG ENORMOUS TURNIP

by Alexei Tolstoy

Illustrated by
Helen Oxenbury

Once upon a time an old man planted a little turnip and said,

"Grow, grow, little turnip, grow sweet.
Grow, grow, little turnip, grow strong."

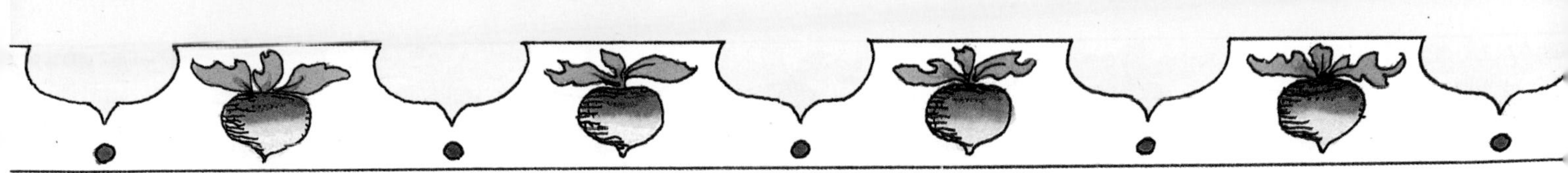

And the turnip grew up sweet and strong, and big and enormous. Then, one day, the old man went to pull it up.

He pulled and pulled again, but he could not pull it up.

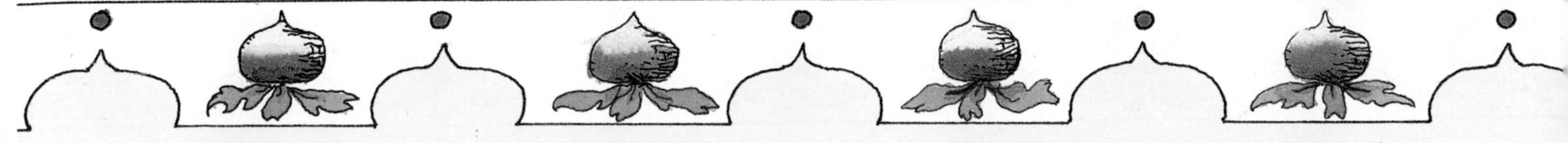

He called the old woman.

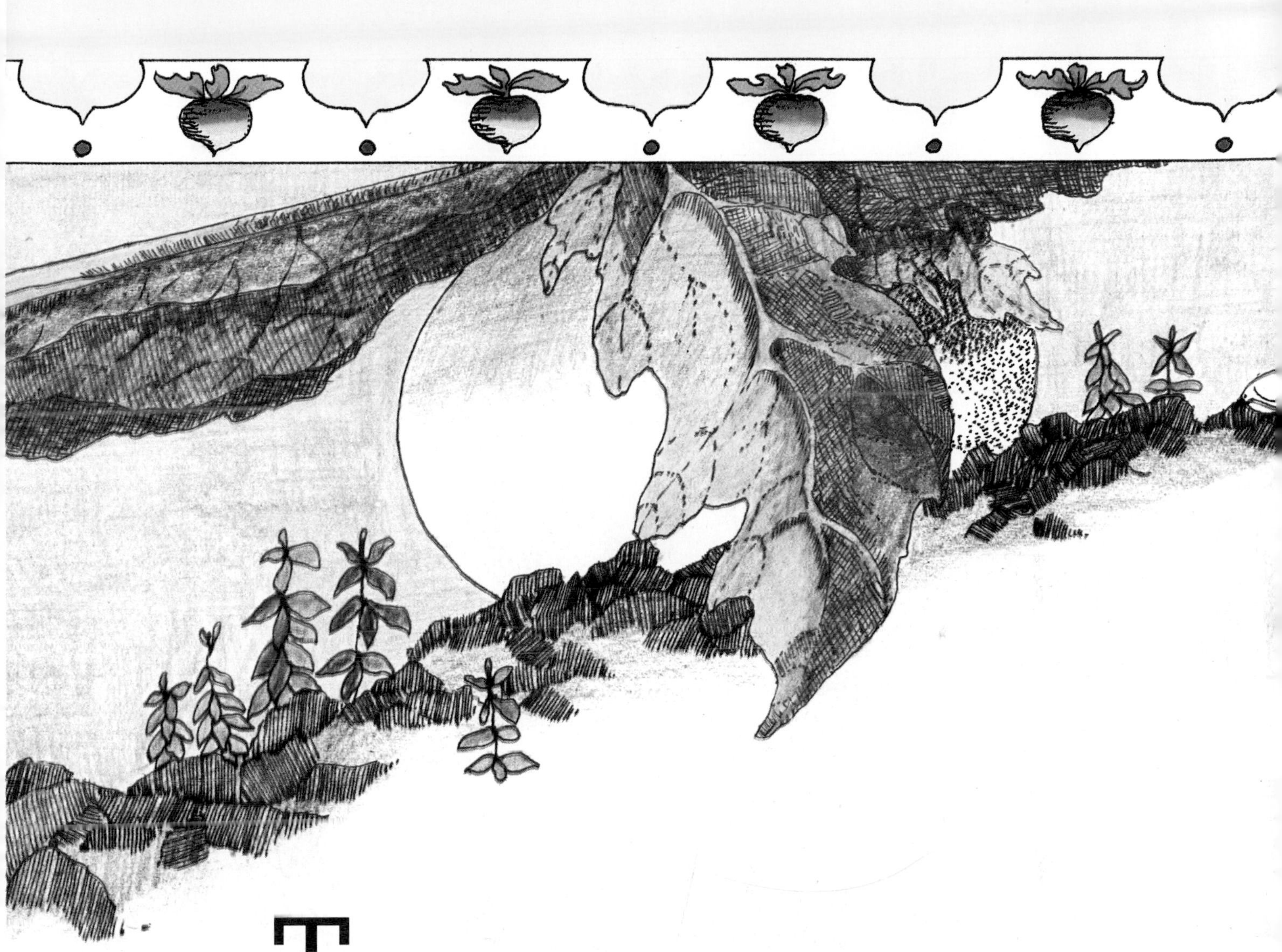

The old woman pulled the old man.
The old man pulled the turnip.
And they pulled and pulled again,
but they could not pull it up.

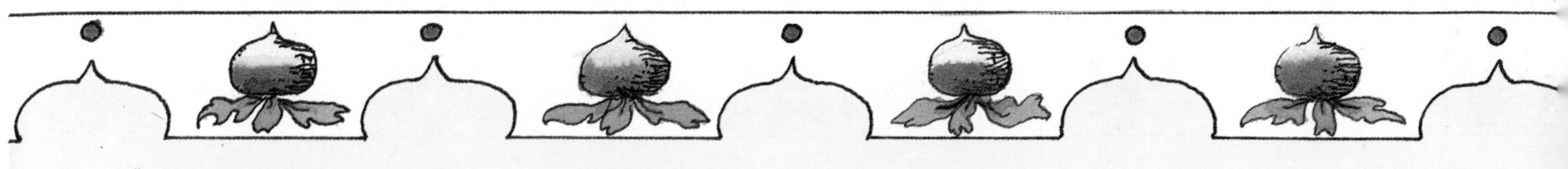

So the old woman called her granddaughter.

The granddaughter pulled the old woman,
the old woman pulled the old man,
the old man pulled the turnip.
And they pulled and pulled again,
but they could not pull it up.

The granddaughter called the black dog.

The black dog pulled the granddaughter,
the granddaughter pulled the old woman,
the old woman pulled the old man,
the old man pulled the turnip.
And they pulled and pulled again,
but they could not pull it up.

The black dog called the cat.

The cat pulled the dog,
the dog pulled the granddaughter,
the granddaughter pulled the old woman,
the old woman pulled the old man,
the old man pulled the turnip.
And they pulled and pulled again,
but still they could not pull it up.

The cat called the mouse.

The mouse pulled the cat,
the cat pulled the dog,
the dog pulled the granddaughter,
the granddaughter pulled the old woman,
the old woman pulled the old man,
the old man pulled the turnip.

They pulled and pulled again, and up came the turnip at last.

Meet Helen Oxenbury

Helen Oxenbury says she first read *The Great Big Enormous Turnip* a very long time ago. Ms. Oxenbury explains that there was one hard thing about making the pictures. "Many of them had to show everyone pulling the turnip," she says. "I didn't want the pictures to get boring because they were all about the same thing. So I showed what the people and animals looked like up close, far away, and from up above."

She'll Be Coming Round the Mountain

1. She'll be coming round the mountain
   when she comes,
   Chug, chug!

   She'll be coming round the mountain
   when she comes,
   Chug, chug!

   She'll be coming round the mountain,
   she'll be coming
   round the mountain,

   She'll be coming round the mountain
   when she comes,
   Chug, chug!

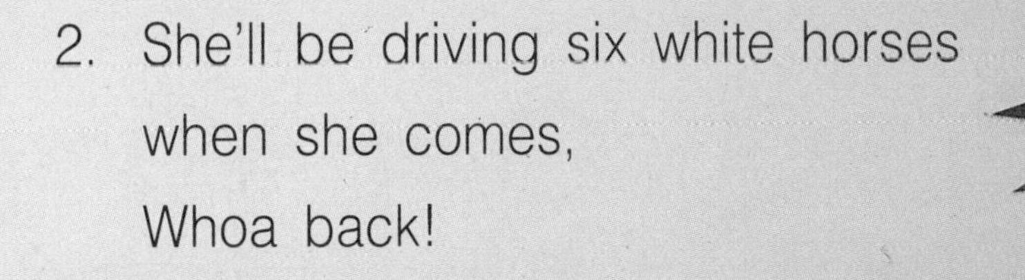

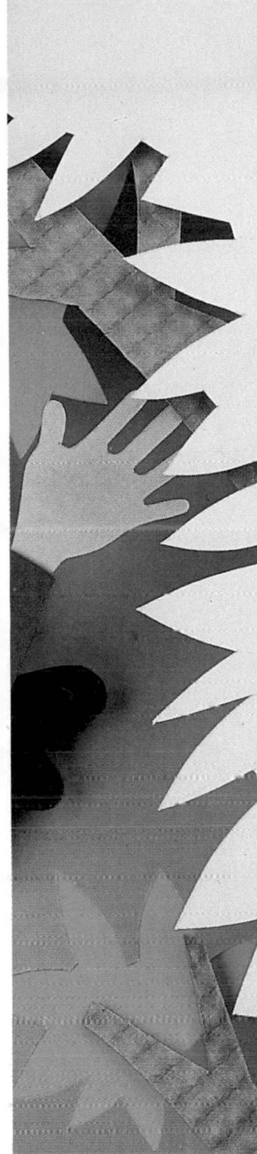

2. She'll be driving six white horses
   when she comes,
   Whoa back!

3. Oh, we'll all go out to meet her
   when she comes,
   Hi, there!

4. She'll be wearing red pajamas
   when she comes,
   Scratch, scratch!

5. Oh, we'll all have chicken and
   dumplin's when she comes,
   Yum, yum!

American Folk Song

THE Missing Tarts

Written By

B. G. Hennessy

Illustrated By

Tracey Campbell Pearson

The Queen of Hearts
She made some tarts
All on a summer's day.

The Knave of Hearts
He stole those tarts
And took them clean away.

"Where are the tarts?"
asked the Queen of Hearts.

"Let's look up the hill,"
said Jack and Jill.

“Not in my bowl,”
said Old King Cole.

"Check the cupboard,"
said Old Mother Hubbard.

"Ask the cat,"
said Jack Sprat.

"Not in my corner,"
said Little Jack Horner.

"Follow that sheep,"
said Little Bo Peep.

“Here’s a clue!”
said Little Boy Blue.

"You'll find them soon,"
said the Man in the Moon.

"They can't be far,"
twinkled the star.

The Queen of Hearts
She found those tarts
All on a summer's day.

The Knave of Hearts
Who took the tarts
Had given them all away!

Meet B. G. Hennessy

As a child, B. G. Hennessy loved nursery rhymes. She says, "I had a collection of nursery rhymes in one book, and I imagined that all the characters lived in one place. When I got older, I thought that was silly. How could they all live together? Later I thought, no, it wouldn't be silly. It would be neat if they all lived together. So I wrote *The Missing Tarts*."

When asked how she gets ideas for her stories, Ms. Hennessy says, "I get my ideas from things I remember when I was five or six years old. You don't have to wait until you are a grown-up to write down your ideas."

Meet Tracey Campbell Pearson

Tracey Campbell Pearson has always loved Mother Goose. She wanted to illustrate *The Missing Tarts* so she could put all the characters together.

Ms. Pearson says, "I wanted to illustrate the real words in the rhymes, but I knew Old King Cole shouldn't be smoking because smoking isn't healthy. So I put in a bubble pipe.

"And every time you see Jack and Jill you know they're going to fall down the hill. So I let them fall down at the beginning of the book. After that was done, they could have fun."

Wee Willie Winkie

Wee Willie Winkie
runs through the town,
Upstairs and downstairs,
in his nightgown,
Rapping at the window,
crying through the lock,
"Are the children in their beds?
Now it's eight o'clock."

Nursery Rhyme

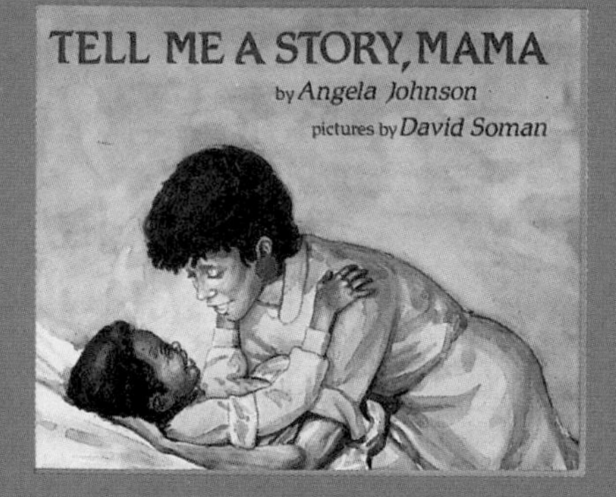

Tell Me a Story, Mama
by Angela Johnson
illustrated by
David Soman
Orchard Books, 1989

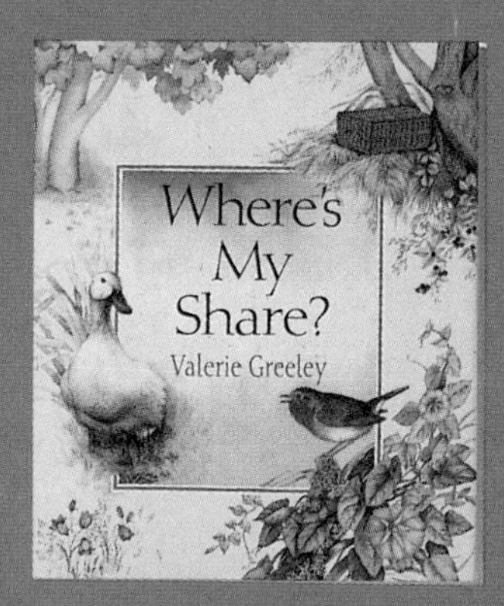

Where's My Share?
written and illustrated
by Valerie Greeley
Macmillan, 1989

10 11 12 13 14 15 16 17 18 19 20 21 22

Meet Pura Belpré

When Pura Belpré was a child in Puerto Rico, she heard many folk tales like "The Bed." "I grew up in a family of storytellers," Ms. Belpré said.

Later Pura Belpré moved to New York City. She worked as a librarian there and told stories to children. But when she looked for folk tales from Puerto Rico to read to them, she couldn't find any.

So she began to write Puerto Rican folk tales. She said, "To see these tales in book form became my dream."

A Puerto Rican folk tale told by Pura Belpré

Illustrated by Catherine Huerta

There was once a little old woman
who had a little boy. He liked to play
under an old-fashioned bed.

But when the bed squeaked, the little boy was
afraid and cried, "Boo, hoo."

And the little old woman ran to him and said,
"Don't cry, little boy.
It's only the sound of this old-fashioned bed."

And this same little old woman bought
a little dog, and gave it to the little boy
for company.

But when the bed squeaked, the dog barked,
"Bow, wow."

The boy cried, "Boo, hoo."

And the little old woman ran to them and said,
"Don't bark, little dog.
Don't cry, little boy.
It's only the sound of this old-fashioned bed."

And this same little old woman bought
a little cat and gave it to the boy
for company.

But when the bed squeaked,
the cat meowed, "Meow, meow."

The dog barked, "Bow, wow."

The boy cried, "Boo, hoo."

And the little old woman ran to them and said,
"Don't meow, little cat.
Don't bark, little dog.
Don't cry, little boy.
It's only the sound of this old-fashioned bed."

And this same little old woman bought
a little mouse and gave it to the boy
for company.

But when the bed squeaked,
the mouse squeaked, "Squeak, squeak."

The cat meowed, "Meow, meow."

The dog barked, "Bow, wow."

The boy cried, "Boo, hoo."

And the little old woman ran to them and said,
"Don't squeak, little mouse.
Don't meow, little cat.
Don't bark, little dog.
Don't cry, little boy.
It's only the sound of this old-fashioned bed."

And this same little old woman bought
a little pig and gave it to the boy
for company.

But when the bed squeaked,
the pig grunted, “Grunt, grunt.”

The mouse squeaked, “Squeak, squeak.”

The cat meowed, “Meow, meow.”

The dog barked, “Bow, wow.”

The boy cried, “Boo, hoo.”

And the little old woman ran to them and said,
"Don't grunt, little pig.
Don't squeak, little mouse.
Don't meow, little cat.
Don't bark, little dog.
Don't cry, little boy.
It's only the sound of this old-fashioned bed."

And one day her little old man came home and stretched out to rest on the old-fashioned bed.

But when the bed squeaked,
he cried, “Ah, Meeeeeeeee.”

The pig grunted, “Grunt, grunt.”

The mouse squeaked, “Squeak, squeak.”

The cat meowed, “Meow, meow.”

The dog barked, “Bow, wow.”

The boy cried, “Boo, hoo.”

And the little old woman ran to them and said,
“Don’t grumble, old man.
Don’t grunt, little pig.
Don’t squeak, little mouse.
Don’t meow, little cat.
Don’t bark, little dog.
Don’t cry, little boy.
It’s only the sound of this old-fashioned bed.”

And just at that moment the old bed broke.

And the little old man fell out.

And the little pig ran away.

And the little mouse scampered away.

And the little cat leaped away.

And the little dog jumped away.

And the little boy was saved.

And the little old woman was so very brave that she just sat on the floor and laughed until she shook.

THE MANY FACES OF THE

Some stories say that wolves eat people, play tricks, and are big, bad, and mean.

Do you know any of these stories?

Many Native American nations admire the wolf. They watched how the wolf lived. They learned from the wolf.

This wolf mask was carved by the Nootka, a Northwest Coast Indian nation.

A wolf is strong.

A wolf is a good hunter.

A wolf lives peacefully with nature.

THE GUNNYWOLF

Retold and illustrated by A. Delaney

Once upon a time, a Little Girl and her father lived next to a deep, dark woods.

The Little Girl never went into the woods.

Nobody did. The Gunnywolf lived there.

But one day, the Little Girl saw a flower blooming just inside the woods.

The Little Girl forgot all about
the Gunnywolf.
She stepped between the trees
and picked the flower.
And she sang,
"A B C D E F G
H I J K L M N O P
Q R S T U V
W X Y Z."

When the Little Girl looked up, she saw more flowers.
Again she forgot about the Gunnywolf.

The Little Girl skipped deeper into the woods and picked the flowers.
And she sang,
"A B C D E F G H I J K L
M N O P Q R S T U V—"

When the Little Girl looked up, she saw even more flowers.

Again she forgot about the Gunnywolf.

The Little Girl ran deep into the woods
and picked the flowers.
And she sang,
"A B C D E F G H I J K L M N O P—"

The Little Girl was far from home.
Holding her flowers, she turned
to go, and—

THERE WAS THE GUNNYWOLF!

"Little Girl!" said the Gunnywolf.
"Sing that good, sweet song to me."

"abcdefghijklmnopqrstuvwxyz,"
sang the Little Girl in a tiny voice.

"M
M
N
A
B,"

sang the Gunnywolf,
and he fell sound asleep.

The Little Girl ran away as fast as she could.
Pit-a-pat, pit-a-pat, pit-a-pat, pit-a-pat!

The Gunnywolf woke up!

Un-ka-cha! Un-ka-cha! Un-ka-cha! Un-ka-cha!
He ran, and soon he caught up with the
Little Girl.

"Little Girl!" said the Gunnywolf.
"Sing that good, sweet song again."

"A B C D E F G H I J K L M
N O P Q R S T U V W X Y Z,"
sang the Little Girl.

“Q
R
L
S
P,”
sang the Gunnywolf,
and he fell sound asleep.

Pit-a-pat, pit-a-pat, pit-a-pat, pit-a-pat!

The Little Girl ran back through the woods as fast as she could.

The Gunnywolf woke up!
Un-ka-cha! Un-ka-cha!
Un-ka-cha! Un-ka-cha!
He ran, and again he caught
up with the Little Girl.

"Little Girl!" said the Gunnywolf.
"Sing that good, sweet song again."

"A B C D E F G H I J K L M N O P Q R S
T U V W X Y Z," sang the Little Girl.

"X
Y
Z
Z
z,"
sang the Gunnywolf,
and he fell sound asleep.

Pit-a-pat, pit-a-pat, pit-a-pat, pit-a-pat!

The Little Girl ran out of the woods.

“Whew!” said the Little Girl.

But the next day and every day after that,
when the Little Girl went outside,

she gathered flowers and more flowers and even more flowers.

And she sang,
"A B C D E F G H I J K L M
N O P Q R S T U V W X Y Z."

Meet A. Delaney

A. Delaney says that *The Gunnywolf* was one of the first stories she heard as a child. "My mother used to tell it to my sister and me. We loved it."

Ms. Delaney explains that there are different ways to tell the story. "When my mother told it, she used her hands," she says. "When the little girl goes 'Pit-a-pat,' she moved her two fingers like two legs running. When the Gunnywolf goes 'Un-ka-cha!,' she made her fist gallop."

There Was a CROOKED Man

There was a crooked man, and he walked a crooked mile,

He found a crooked sixpence against a crooked stile;

He bought a crooked cat, which caught a crooked mouse,

And they all lived together in a little crooked house.

Nursery Rhyme

I'll Tell You a Story

I'll tell you a story

About Jack a Nory,

And now my story's begun;

I'll tell you another

About Jack and his brother,

And now my story is done.

Nursery Rhyme

CONTENTS

UNIT
2
Just Imagine!

The Butterfly

Up and down the air you float
Like a little fairy boat;
I should like to sail the sky,
Gliding like a butterfly!

CLINTON SCOLLARD

IN THE ATTIC

by Hiawyn Oram
illustrated by Satoshi Kitamura

hi
every body love EVERYBODY
PARTY

I had a million toys, but I was bored.

So I climbed into the attic.

The attic was empty.

Or was it?

ABC
DEFGH

I found a family of mice . . .

. . . and a cool, quiet place to rest and think.

I met a spider and we made a web.

I opened windows to other worlds.

I found an old flying machine

and I made it work.

I went out to look for someone

to share what I had found . . .

. . . and I found a friend I could talk to.

My friend and I found a game that could

go on forever, but it was time for dinner.

So I climbed out of the attic, and
told my mother where I'd been all day.

"But we don't have an attic,"
she said.

I guess she doesn't know about the attic.

She hasn't found the ladder.

Meet Hiawyn Oram

Hiawyn Oram grew up in South Africa. She says, "We had no TV. All the best games I played were games of make-believe. I played them alone or with my friends. We pretended we could do anything." She adds, "*In the Attic* is about the wonderful things we make up in our minds."

Meet Satoshi Kitamura

Satoshi Kitamura says his idea for *In the Attic* has a hidden joke in it. "The attic is the place at the top of the house where you put all the things you don't use. The brain is the place at the top of your head where you put ideas you don't always use! So I imagined a boy going into his attic and, using his imagination, finding all kinds of things."

By Myself

When I'm by myself
And I close my eyes
I'm a twin
I'm a dimple in a chin
I'm a room full of toys
I'm a squeaky noise
I'm a gospel song
I'm a gong
I'm a leaf turning red
I'm a loaf of brown bread
I'm a whatever I want to be
An anything I care to be
And when I open my eyes
What I care to be
Is me

Eloise Greenfield
Illustrated by Leo and Diane Dillon

MEET ANN JONAS

When Ann Jonas was a child, she sometimes saw animal shapes in things around her. Today she still does. She got the idea for *The Trek* when she passed a fruit stand. "I saw a cut watermelon there," she says. "To me, it looked like a hippopotamus's mouth."

Pictures in *The Trek* show real places and people in Ms. Jonas's neighborhood. The man walking a dog is her husband, Donald Crews. Her two daughters are the girls jogging in the park, and the house with the cat in the window is her house.

THE TREK

by Ann Jonas

My mother
doesn't walk me
to school anymore.

But she doesn't know
we live on the edge
of a jungle.

She doesn't even see
what's right outside our door!

There are creatures everywhere.
But they can't hide from me.

BUS
STOP

Some of my animals are dangerous
and it's only my amazing skill
that saves me day after day.

Look at that!

The waterhole is really crowded today.

What will they do when this herd
goes down to drink?

Here's my helper, right on time.
Now we can cross the desert together.

Those animals won't see us
if we stay behind the sand dunes.
Be very quiet.

That woman doesn't know
about the animals.
If she did, she'd be scared.

We missed the boat!
Now we'll have to swim
across the river.

COIN
OPERATED

FRUIT &
Garden
Tomatoes

Be careful! This jungle is full of animals.

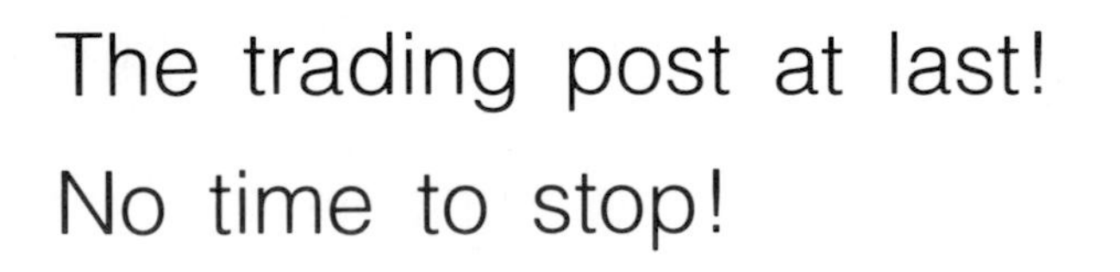

The trading post at last!
No time to stop!

COFFEE SHOPPE

We're almost there,
only the mountain
to climb.

We made it!

Where Go the Boats?

Dark brown is the river,
    Golden is the sand.
It flows along forever,
    With trees on either hand.

Green leaves a-floating,
    Castles of the foam,
Boats of mine a-boating—
    Where will all come home?

On goes the river,
    And out past the mill,
Away down the valley,
    Away down the hill.

Away down the river,
    A hundred miles or more,
Other little children
    Shall bring my boats ashore.

Robert Louis Stevenson

WHAT
DO
YOU
SEE?

It Looked Like Spilt Milk
written and illustrated by
Charles G. Shaw
Harper Trophy, 1988

This Can Lick
a Lollipop
Body Riddles for Kids
Esto goza chupando
un caramelo
Las partes del cuerpo en
adivinanzas infantiles
English words by Joel Rothman
Spanish words by Argentina Palacios
Photographs by Patricia Ruben

This Can Lick a Lollipop
by Joel Rothman and
Argentina Palacios
photos by Patricia Ruben
Doubleday, 1979

Meet Peter and Susan Barrett

Peter and Susan Barrett are a husband-and-wife team who usually write books for adults. *The Line Sophie Drew* is their best-known children's book.

THE LINE SOPHIE DREW

By Peter and Susan Barrett

Once upon a time there was a little girl called Sophie who drew a line.

Along came Laura who said,
"It's the sea with a boat on it."

"No it isn't," said Sophie.

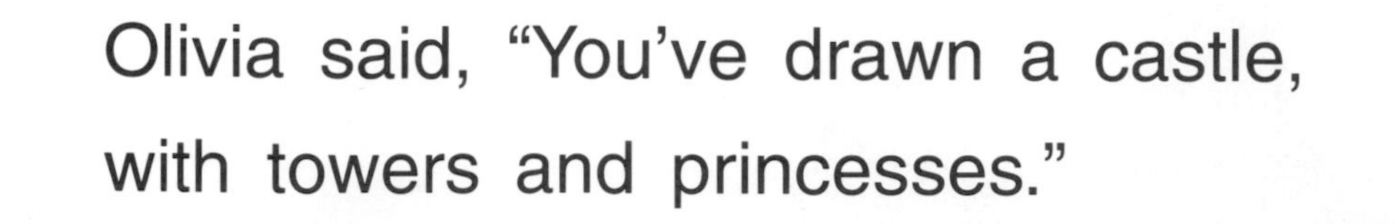

Olivia said, "You've drawn a castle, with towers and princesses."

Sophie said she hadn't.

Then, along came Alexander.
"Oh look," said Alexander,
"a spikey dragon breathing fire!"

"No it isn't," said Sophie.

Sarah said it was a thick dark forest with tall trees and strange birds.

"No it isn't," said Sophie.

Vicky looked at it a long time and saw a huge table covered with food for a party.

"It's not a party," said Sophie.

Graham thought it was the place under the sea where there are fish with legs.

"Don't be silly," said Sophie.

“It’s a long line of dwarfs in pointed pink hats,” said Ben.

“It’s not dwarfs,” said Sophie.

Marcus turned it upside down and said it was a space station, halfway between Earth and Mars.

"It's not a space station," said Sophie.

Sophie's father said, "Let's make it into butterflies."

"Let's not," said Sophie.

“That’s a nice wiggly line,”
said Sophie’s mother.

"It's not a line," said Sophie.
"It's something I'm thinking of."

What do <u>you</u> think it is?

LiNES, LiNES, AND MORE LiNES!

Artists use lines when they draw.

Straight lines.

Curving lines.

Thick lines.

Thin lines.

What kinds of lines do *you* see?

Children Carrying Packages by Paul Klee

Untitled by Keith Haring

Fishing Boats at Sea by Vincent Van Gogh

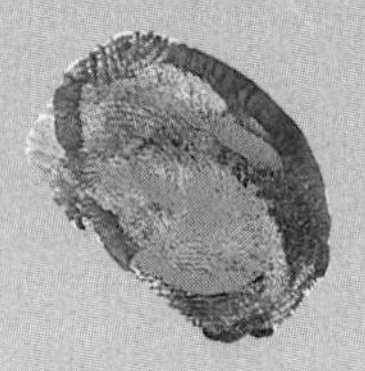

Pat Cummings

Pat Cummings laughs when she tells why she wrote *Jimmy Lee Did It*. "When I was growing up, if something in our house got broken or disappeared, my younger brother Artie always blamed it on someone named Jimmy Lee. I never saw Jimmy Lee or heard Jimmy Lee, so I thought writing this book might be a good way to get back at Artie. I thought it would be a good joke."

Jimmy Lee Did It

By Pat Cummings

Jimmy Lee is back again
And nothing is the same.

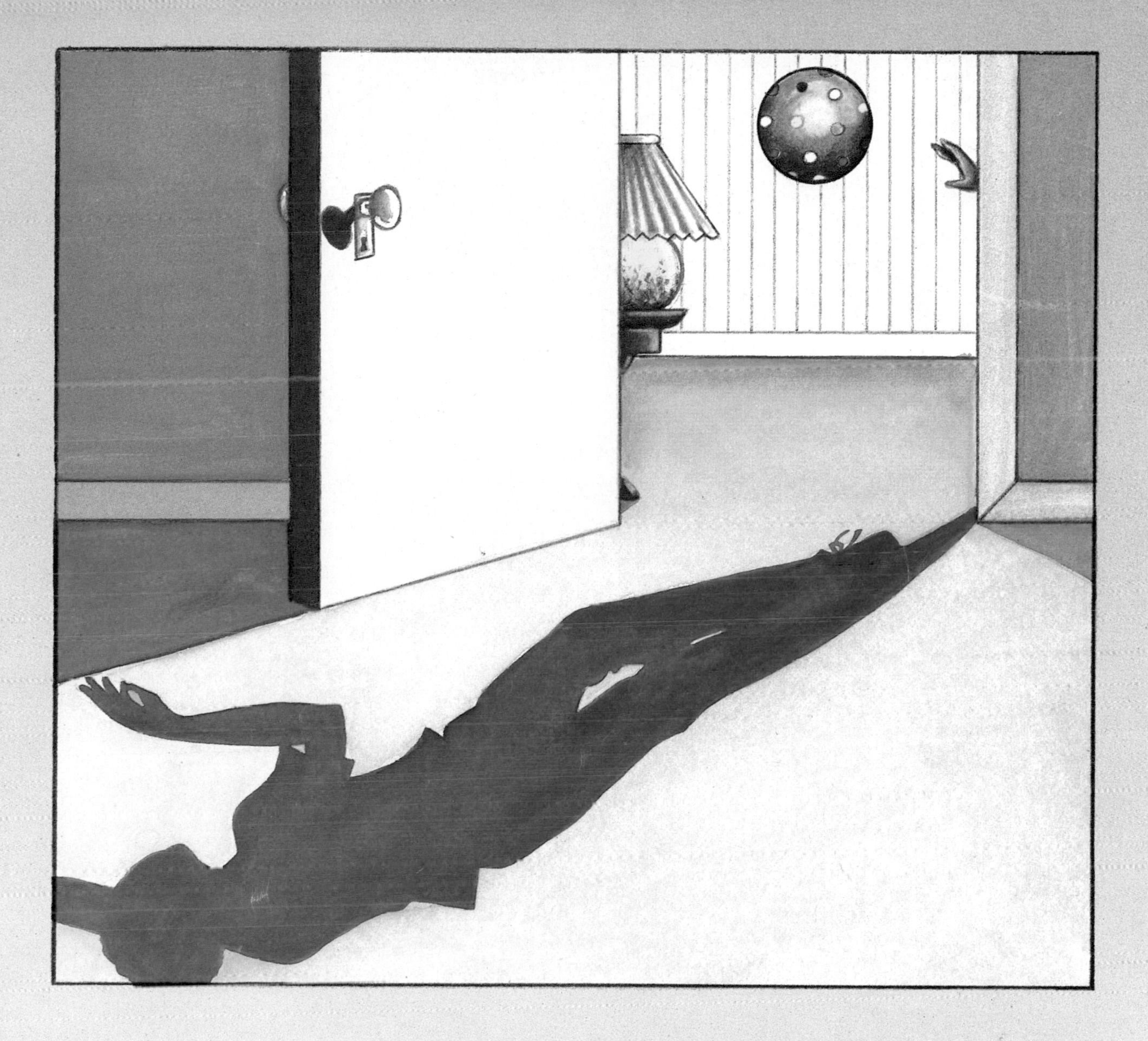

He's causing lots of trouble,
While my brother takes the blame.

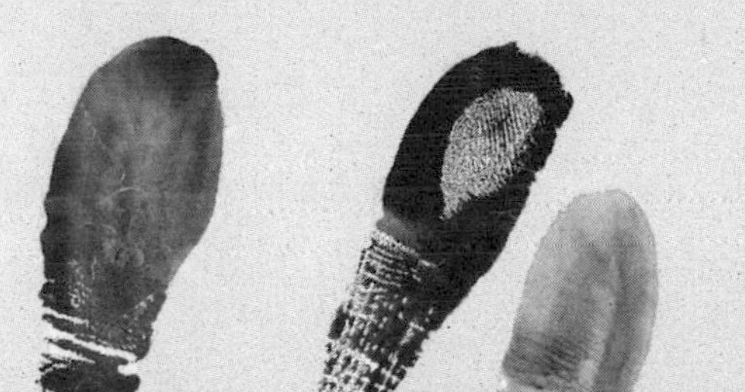

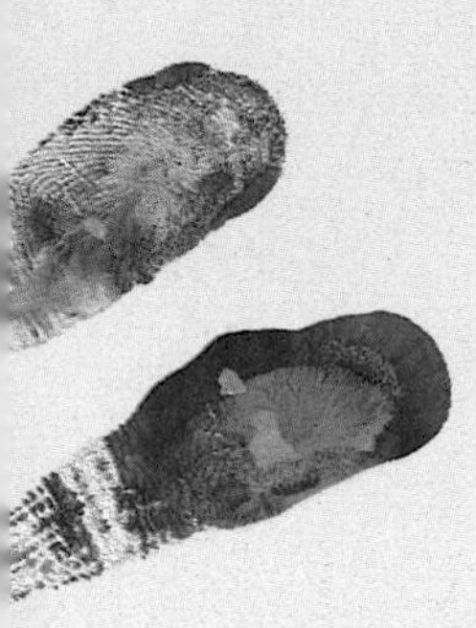

Artie made his bed, he said.
But Jimmy thinks he's smart.

While Artie read his comics,
Jimmy pulled the sheets apart.

Dad fixed us pancakes
And Artie said his tasted fine,

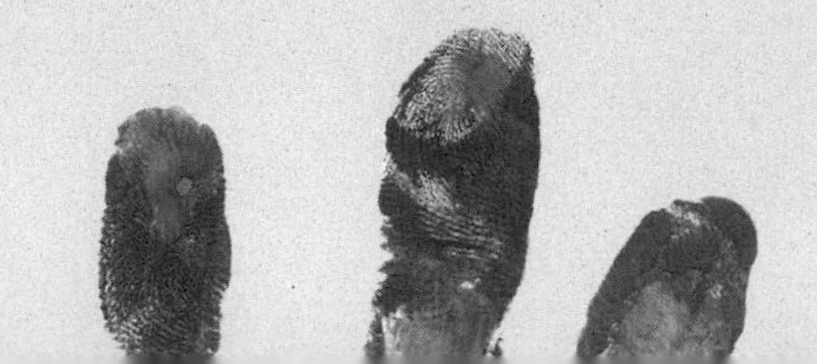

But Jimmy Lee had just been there
And eaten most of mine.

I heard the crash of breaking glass,
But turned too late, I guess.

"Jimmy Lee did it," Artie said,
As we cleaned up the mess.

When Artie's room got painted,
Jimmy Lee was in the hall.

He used up Artie's crayons
Drawing pictures on the wall.

And when I finally found my bear,
I asked Artie, "Who hid it?"

He told me frankly, “Angel,
It was Jimmy Lee who did it.”

He caused so much trouble
That I began to see—

The only way to stop it
Was to capture Jimmy Lee.

I knew about his sweet tooth,
So I set a tasty trap,

But Jimmy Lee just waited
Till I had to take my nap.

I spread out all my marbles
To trip up Jimmy Lee.

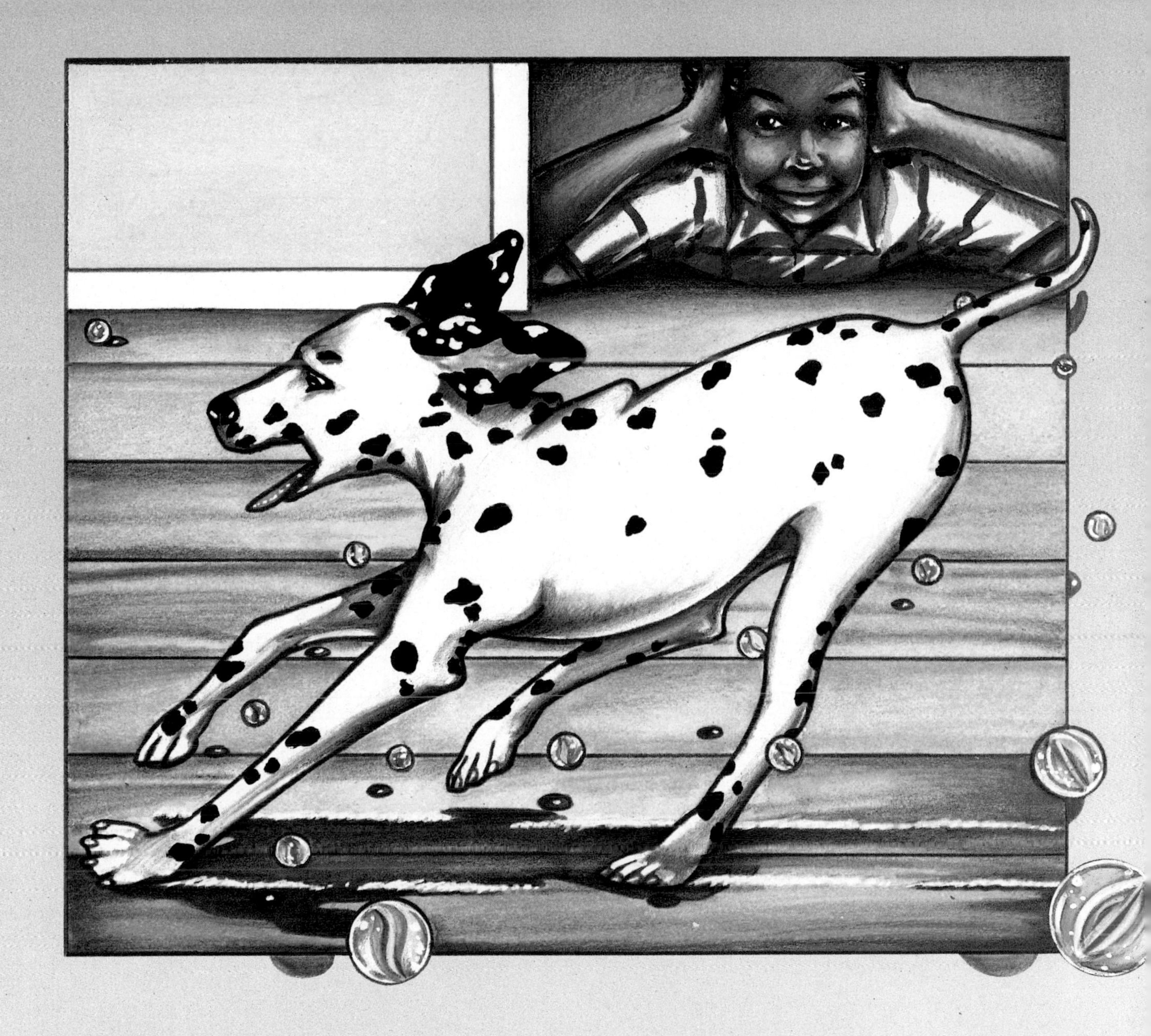

The dog slid by and scratched the floor
And Mom got mad at me.

I hid in the hall closet
And I never made a sound,

But Jimmy Lee will only come
When Artie is around.

I don't know what he looks like,
He never leaves a trace—

Except for spills and tears
And Artie's things about the place.

Since Artie won't describe him,
He remains a mystery.

But if you're smart, you'll listen
And watch out for Jimmy Lee.

PRETENDING

When you are in bed and it's cold outside,
do you ever pretend that you have to hide?
Do you curl up your toes?
Do you wrinkle your nose?
Do you make yourself little so none of you shows?

Do you pull the sheets over the whole of your face
and pretend you are in some faraway place?
Mother thinks you are sleeping,
but she does not know
that all tucked in your bed, you have places to go.

Bobbi Katz

INFORMATION ILLUSTRATED

A GUIDE TO SKILLS AND INFORMATION SOURCES THAT GO WITH THE STORIES YOU ARE READING!

CONTENTS

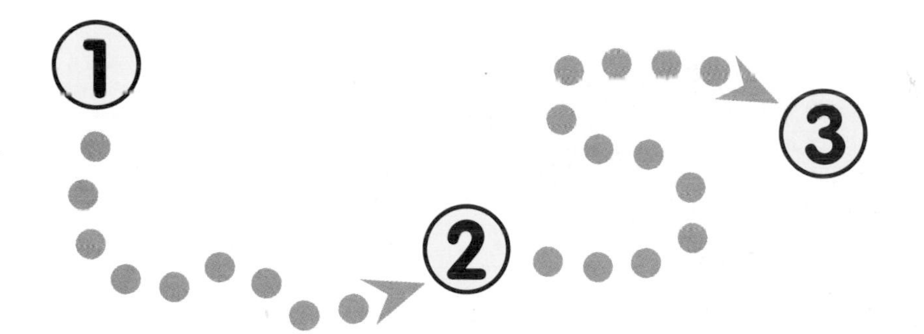

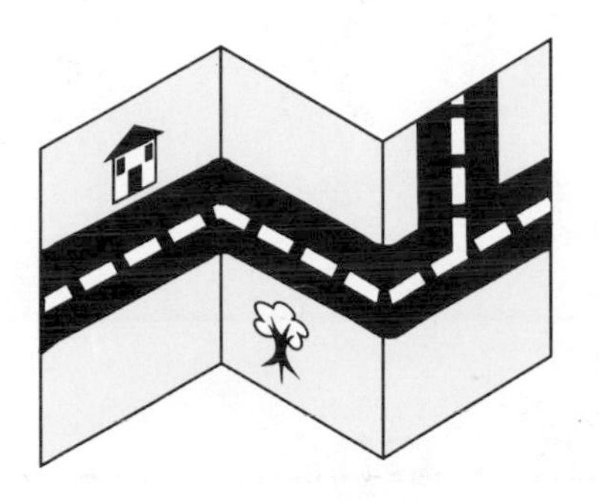

BOOK PARTS

A BOOK
OF
FAIRY TALES

Hans Christian Andersen

◆

MANGUS & COMPANY
Beaver Creek, Kansas

Title Page

BOOK PARTS

CONTENTS

Table of Contents

DIRECTIONS

ANIMAL MASKS

Use your imagination to make an animal mask. Here's what you will need:

- a large paper bag
- scissors
- glue
- construction paper
- crayons, felt-tip pens, or magic markers

HERE'S WHAT TO DO:

1.

First, put the paper bag over your head and have a friend make marks for eye holes and arm holes.

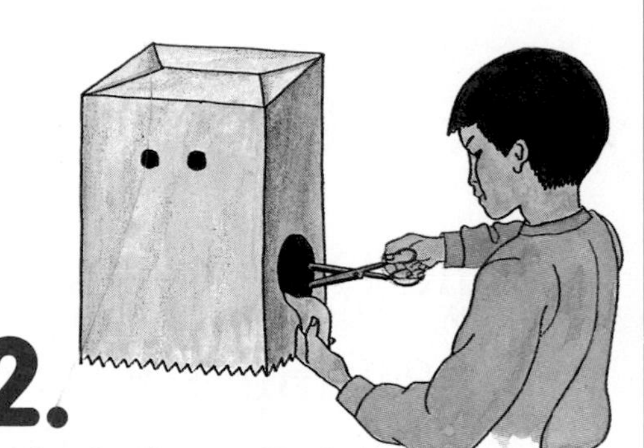

2.

Take the bag off. Then, cut holes for your eyes and arms.

3.

Now draw and color eyes and mouth.

4.

Next, make ears, nose, and other parts from construction paper. Glue them to the paper bag.

5.

Finally, you may want to add other things — like feathers or straws.

DIRECTIONS

CLAY DOUGH

Clay dough is soft. It can easily be made into many different shapes.
You can buy clay dough, but you can also make it. Here is what you will need:

- flour
- water
- salt
- vegetable oil
- a large bowl
- measuring cups

DIRECTIONS FOR MAKING CLAY DOUGH

1. Mix 1 1/2 cups of flour and 1/2 cup of salt in a bowl.

2. Stir in 1/2 cup of water and 1/2 cup of vegetable oil.

3. Squeeze the mixture with your hands for 3 or 4 minutes. Wet your hands if the mixture doesn't hold together. When it feels like clay, it is ready to use.

Clay dough is fun to play with. You can roll it, pat it, flatten it, pinch it, and mold it however you want. You can make anything you want—real or imaginary—out of clay dough.

MAPS

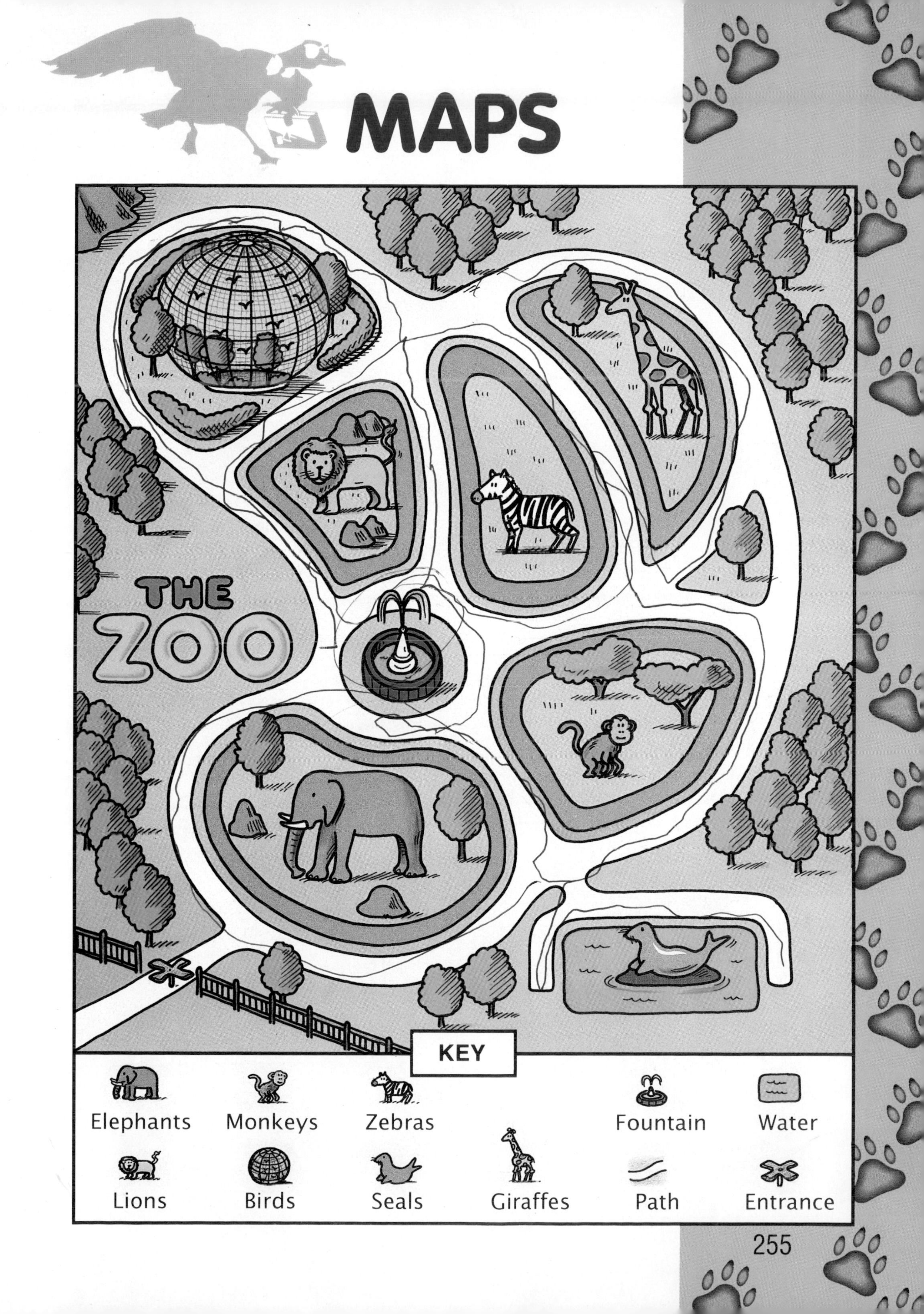
MAPS
THE ZOO
KEY
Elephants
Monkeys
Zebras
Fountain
Water
Lions
Birds
Seals
Giraffes
Path
Entrance

Glos

This glossary can help you to find out the meanings of words in this book that you may not know.

sary

The words are listed in alphabetical order. Guide words at the top of each page tell you the first and last words on the page.

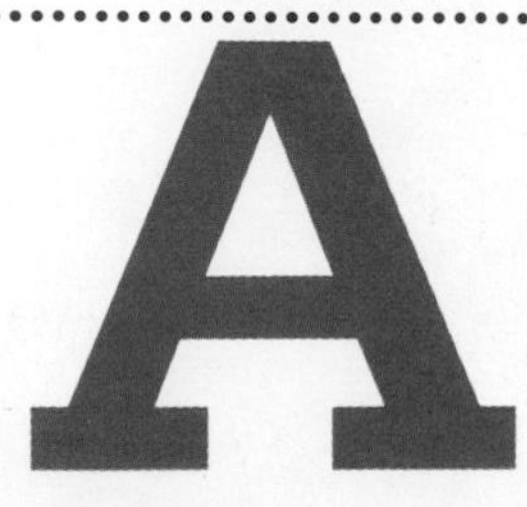

amazing

When something is **amazing,** it is very surprising. The rocket blasted off with **amazing** speed.

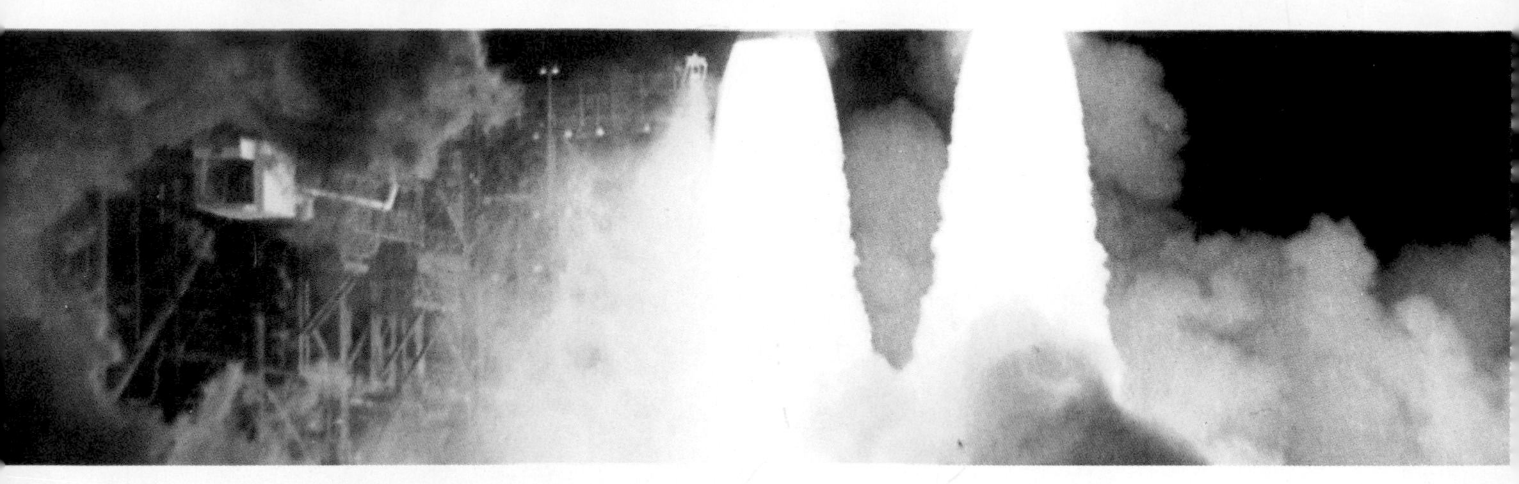

blame

Blame means the cause of something wrong or bad. Ed took the **blame** for letting the dog get mud on the floor.

capture

Capture means to catch and hold a person, animal, or thing. The children will **capture** the butterfly and then let it go. ▲ **captured, capturing.**

company

Company means having a person or animal with you so you do not feel alone. When no one is home with Dad, Rex keeps him **company.**

cupboard

A **cupboard** is a closet with shelves to store dishes or food. There are plates, cups, and bowls in the **cupboard.**
▲ **cupboards.**

D

dragon

A **dragon** is a make-believe animal that is big and scary. This **dragon** has wings and a long tail. ▲ **dragons.**

dwarf

A **dwarf** is a tiny make-believe man who has magical powers. We read a fairy tale about a **dwarf** who could turn straw into gold. ▲ **dwarfs** or **dwarves.**

enormous

Enormous means huge or giant in size. The blue whale is an **enormous** animal.

gather

Gather means to bring together. The children **gather** wood for the fire. ▲ **gathered, gathering.**

herd

A **herd** is a group of animals that live or travel together. A **herd** of elephants is taking a bath. ▲ **herds.**

jungle

A **jungle** is a place where many trees and plants grow. It is hot and rains a lot in a **jungle.** Monkeys, snakes, and parrots live in the **jungle.** ▲ **jungles.**

million

A **million** is a very large number. It looks as if there are a **million** stars in the sky. ▲ **millions.**

old-fashioned

Old-fashioned means not new, or out-of-date. The woman wore an **old-fashioned** dress that belonged to her grandmother.

spider

A **spider** is a kind of bug that has eight legs. A **spider** can spin a web.
▲ **spiders.**

tower

A **tower** is a tall, narrow part on top of a building. The castle had a **tower** on each side. ▲ **towers.**

turnip

A **turnip** is a round vegetable that is yellow or white. A large **turnip** grew in the garden.

▲ **turnips.**

W

waterhole

A **waterhole** is a place where animals gather to drink water. Zebras, elephants, and giraffes drink at the waterhole. ▲ **waterholes.**

Claudia Karabaic Sargent, 94-95, 98, 104-107, 109, 111-112, 119, 122-123 (borders); Andy Levine, 124-125. **Unit 2:** Delana Bettoli, 126-129; Wendy Edelson, 192-193; Vera Rosenberry, 246-247 (bkgd.). **Information Illustrated:** Loretta Lustig, 250-251; George Poladian, 252-253; Patrick Merrell, 254-255. **Glossary:** Scott Webber, 258; Robbin Gourley, 259 (m); Robert Pepper, 259 (b); Dave Maloney, 260; Lionel Kalish, 261; Jean Stephens, 263.

PHOTOGRAPHY CREDITS

All photographs are by the Macmillan/McGraw-Hill School Division (MMSD) except as noted below.

Unit 1: 41: Courtesy of Helen Oxenbury. 74: Courtesy of B. G. Hennessy. 75: Courtesy of Tracey Campbell Pearson. 78-79: Lissa Rovetch, 92: t. Gary Milburn/Tom Stack & Associates; b. Philip Gifford, Courtesy Dept. of Library Services, American Museum of Natural History. 93: t. Zig Leszczynski/Animals, Animals; b. Jim Brandenburg/Minden Pictures. **Unit 2:** 157: t.r. Hiawyn Oram; b.l. Anderson Press Ltd. 160: Scott Harvey for MMSD. 194-195: Jay Alan Lefcowitz. 218: Kunstsammiung Nordhrhein-Westfalen. 219: Musees Royaux des Beaux-Arts de Belgique Bruxelles (Photo: G. Cussac). 256 l. Roy Morsch/The Stock Market; r. Francois Gohier/Photo Researchers. 257-258; Hank Morgan/Science Source/Photo Researchers. 259: Myrleen Ferguson/PhotoEdit. 260: Francois Gohier/Photo Researchers, Inc. 261: F. S. Mitchell/Tom Stack & Associates. 262: t. Roy Morsch/The Stock Market: b. Photri/The Stock Market. 263: Bo Zaunders/The Stock Market.